Pete and Perky

Special Words

Special words help make this story fun.
Your child may need help reading them.

cage

door

Mrs.

noise

parrot

phone

screech

talk

Pete and Perky

Written by Mary Hooper
Illustrated by Lucy Su

Hooked On Phonics®

Hooked On Phonics®

Contents

1. A Very Smart Bird

"Be careful, Pete," Mrs. Smith
called from the door.

Pete had stopped in to see
Mrs. Smith on his way to school.
He turned and shut her gate.

"Take care!" Mrs. Smith said.

"Take care!" Perky said too.

Perky was Mrs. Smith's parrot. He was perched on a stand outside her door. He liked to sit there and watch the children go by.

"Watch for the cars," Mrs. Smith said.

"Watch for the cars!" said Perky.

Pete went to the crosswalk, smiling to himself. Mrs. Smith and Perky were always telling him to put on his jacket or to watch for cars.

Pete had been pals with
Mrs. Smith and Perky for a year.
They started talking because of a
project at school about the war.

Everyone had to find someone
old and talk to them about what
life was like in World War Two.

Pete's mom had asked
Mrs. Smith to help him.

Pete had not wanted to go
to see her in the beginning, but
Mrs. Smith had lots of tales to
tell that were funny. And she
had Perky too! Perky had been
Mr. Smith's pet.

Mr. Smith had been a sailor and had gotten Perky when he was overseas.

Perky was red and green. He had a big cage, and he also had a perch that could go all over the house.

Sometimes, when he was sitting outside on the perch, Perky did tricks. He could swing on his perch or hang upside down and screech.

"He wants you to look at him," Mrs. Smith would say.

Perky could make all kinds of noises too. He could make a noise like a phone ringing,

or a dog barking,

or a baby crying.

He could even sing like a canary
he had seen on TV!

Best of all, he could talk.

Mrs. Smith showed him how to
say lots of words, even people's
names. He also said things like
"Shut the door!" and "Where's
supper?" and "Have a good day!"

Mr. Smith had showed him how to say lots of funny words too.

That day, Pete had been at Mrs. Smith's house to bring Perky some seeds.

He waved to Mrs. Smith and
Perky and crossed the road at the
crosswalk.

"Be careful!" Mrs. Smith called.
"Be careful!" Perky said too.

Pete smiled. He would be very careful all right. With Perky and Mrs. Smith watching him, he had to!

2. A Good Trick

"Perky has a new trick!"
Mrs. Smith said to Pete.

Pete had stopped in to see
them on his way home from
school. Perky was sitting on top
of his cage.

"A new trick?" Pete asked.
"What is it?"

"Well," said Mrs. Smith, "the phone rang yesterday when I was upstairs. I am a bit slow coming down."

Pete nodded.

"Well, all the way down I was calling, 'Hang on, hang on!'"

Pete grinned.

"And then, just as I got there, the ringing stopped. And what do you think happened?"

"What?" said Pete.

"Well," said Mrs. Smith, "it had stopped ringing because Perky had picked up the phone. He hit the handset off with his beak! And then do you know what he said?"

"What?" said Pete.

" 'Hang on! Hang on!' " Mrs. Smith said.

Perky gave a loud screech and banged on the top of the cage with his beak.

"Hang on! Hang on!" he called.

"See!" said Mrs. Smith. "What do you think of that?"

"Fantastic!" Pete said. "Perky could go on TV. Do you think he will do it again?"

"I do not know," Mrs. Smith said. "My sister's call is the one phone call I have had all week."

"Why not try now?" Pete asked. "I will call you. Then we will know!"

Mrs. Smith nodded. "Oh, yes," she said. "Go to the public phone at the end of the road." She lowered her voice. "I will go upstairs and pretend to be busy. When the phone rings, we will see if Perky picks it up again!"

Mrs. Smith gave Pete her number and 35 cents.

"Be careful," she called from the door.

"Be careful!" Perky screeched from inside.

He ran to the phone and called Mrs. Smith. Her phone began to ring: 6 times...10 times...20 times. Pete was about to give up.

Then there was a thud as the phone hit something.

Perky said, "Hang on! Hang on!"

"Perky," Pete yelled. "Hang on! Hang on!"

Pete ran back to Mrs. Smith's house as fast as he could.

"Perky is the smartest bird in the world!" he said.

"Well, I think so too," said Mrs. Smith.

Then Pete looked at his watch.

"I have to go," he said. "And next week there is no school, so I will not see you for a while."

Mrs. Smith went with him to the door.

"Have a good time," she said, "and be careful!"

"Be careful!" Perky screeched.

3. The Big Move

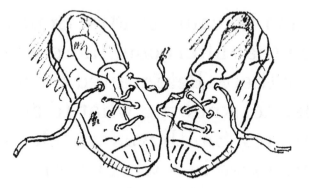

Pete did not see Mrs. Smith or Perky for a week. He wanted to drop in first thing on his way to school, but he had lost his sneakers. By the time he got them, he was late for school and there was no time.

When he came to Mrs. Smith's house that afternoon, there was a doctor there. Pete waited for a while, not knowing what to do. Then Mrs. Smith was wheeled out of the house in a wheelchair.

Mrs. Smith looked very pale. She had her eyes shut and her legs were under a red blanket.

"Can I talk to her?" Pete asked.

"Yes, you can," said the doctor.

That's when Mrs. Smith looked up at him.

"Pete," she said.

"What happened?" Pete asked. "Is your leg broken or something?"

Mrs. Smith said, "No, but I fell down the stairs."

"Where are you going?"
Pete asked.

"I will be living in a home for
old people," she said.

Pete did not know what to say.
Then he remembered Perky.

"What about Perky?" he asked. "Who is going to look after him?"

"He will be going down to the pet shop," said the doctor. "We will find a good home for him."

Mrs. Smith suddenly grabbed Pete's arm.

"I want you to have him!" she said.

Pete gasped.

"I do not know what my mom would say."

"You know how to look after him," Mrs. Smith said. "You know what he likes."

Pete could not remember if his mom liked parrots. She did not care when he took the hamsters home from school and when they looked after his pal's dog.

But he did not know about a big, screeching bird.

"You can bring him to see me in the old people's home," Mrs. Smith said. "The old people will like that!"

Pete did not want Perky to go to a pet shop where anyone could buy him.

He said, "Yes, I will take him! Can I take him now?"

Mrs. Smith nodded. "I know he will be OK with you," she said.

"Better go and get him before we shut the house up," said the doctor.

Pete watched as Mrs. Smith was put into the white car.

"Come and see me. And be careful!"

"You be careful too," said Pete. Then he went into the house to get Perky.

Perky was in his cage. He looked at Pete sadly.

"You are coming home with me!" Pete said. "Are your things packed?"

Perky did not say a thing. Pete got Perky's stand. He picked up Perky's cage. He put Perky's seeds in a bag. Then he went home.

4. A Sad Pet

Two weeks went by, and Pete
and his mom were watching TV.
Perky was in his cage by the
window. He was not looking out,
and he was not looking at the TV.
He was just looking at the wall.

"What's the matter with Perky?"
said Pete.

"I think he's sad," his mom said.
"He misses Mrs. Smith."

"Can I take him to see her?"
Pete asked.

"Yes," said Mom, "but it is miles
away. When the holidays come,
perhaps."

Pete looked at Perky. "That's a
long time."

"Did you say he liked to talk a lot?" Mom asked.

"All the time! He would say just what Mrs. Smith said, and he could say things on his own too. He made noises—all kinds of noises. And he could even pick up the phone."

Mom went up to Perky's cage. "Good birdy! Can I have a kiss?" she said.

Perky did not say a thing.

"Be careful," Pete said to Perky. "Watch out for the cars."

Perky did not say a thing. He did not even look up.

"He must be very, very sad," Pete said.

"Maybe we need to take Perky to the vet," Mom said. "He's not talking, and he does not eat very much."

"Can a vet fix birds?" Pete asked.

"You bet," Mom said.

Pete handed Perky a seed.

"Be careful!" he said. "Watch out for the vet!"

But Perky did not say anything at all.

5. Clever Bird!

Pete was in the living room reading.

Perky was on the bottom of his cage, looking at the wall.

Pete and his mom had been to the vet with Perky.

"He's fine," she had said when she checked him over.

"I think he's just a bit sad."

"Will he be OK? Do you think he will talk again?" Pete had asked her.

"I just do not know," she said. "I do not think there's anything we can do to make him talk. If he wants to talk, he will."

Pete stopped reading and went over to Perky.

"Do you want to sit on your stand?" he asked. He put the stand where Perky could see it.

"Come out and talk to me!" Pete put his hand in Perky's cage to pick him up.

Perky backed away from
Pete's hand. He went to the side
of the cage where Pete could not
reach him.

"Oh, come on!" Pete said. "Talk to me! Say funny things like you did before."

Perky turned his back on Pete.

Pete sadly shut the cage. He switched on the TV and went back to sit down to watch a cartoon. He did not look at Perky for a while.

All of a sudden—just when the cartoon was getting really good—Perky jumped up on his perch.

He looked at Pete.

"Take care! Be careful!" he screeched. Then he began running back and forth, bobbing his head up and down.

Pete ran over to him. "Perky, you are talking!"

Then, before Pete could sit back down, or even blink, there was a screech of brakes from outside the house—then a ripping noise, like a gate being torn down—then a really big crash!

Bricks started tumbling all over, and a car crashed into the wall, hitting the chair where Pete had just been sitting.

Pete yelled.

Perky screeched.

Pete's mom ran in, yelling.

And for a long time, everything was a mess.

"I could not make the turn," the driver of the car said. He was not hurt, just upset. "The road was slippery, and I could feel myself sliding across it. I could not stop. The next thing I knew I was in your living room."

"That's a difficult turn," said the policeman. "It was lucky you were not sitting on that chair, Pete."

"But I was! I was sitting on it just before the crash," Pete said.

"Then my parrot screeched to tell me to get away!"

"Oh, yes?" said the policeman, grinning.

Pete's mom hugged him.

"That's just what he did!" she said.

"He said, 'Take care! Be careful!' " said Pete.

"Be careful! Be careful!" said Perky. Then Perky made a noise just like the police car.

"That's very funny, Perky," Pete said.

When Pete went to see
Mrs. Smith to tell her what
happened, she said, "I always said
he was a clever bird!" She patted
Perky's back. "He is cleverer than
most people!"

"I think so too," said Pete.

Pete and Perky went to see Mrs. Smith quite a lot after that. And Perky never stopped talking and making noises ever again. He was very good at making a noise just like a car crashing into the wall....